Blessed Sebastian
and the Oxen

by
EVA K. BETZ

Illustrations by Charles B. Vukovich

St. Anthony Guild Press
Paterson, New Jersey

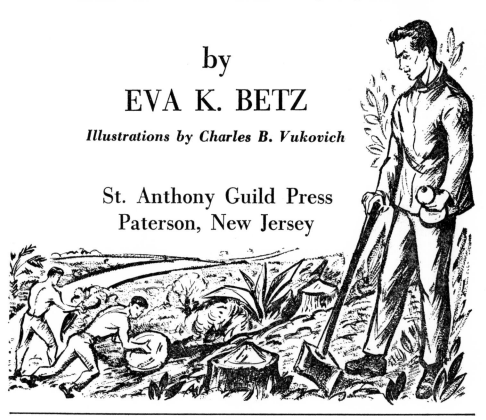

Easy Reading Books of
SAINTS AND FRIENDLY BEASTS

For

My Franciscan Friends

With Respectful Affection

SEBASTIAN sat down in the middle of the sunny field
and looked around him. After a long spell of rain, the grass
and flowers seemed as glad to see the sun as he was. The
sheep that Sebastian was tending scrunch-scrunched as they
chewed the sweet clover. When a bird flew up from the
ground in front of them, the baby lambs pretended to be
very frightened and ran to their mammas as fast as they
could go.

A little bright-eyed field mouse peeked around a big daisy.
When it saw Sebastian sitting on the ground it did not run
away but went up quite close to him. It stood there wiggling
its whiskers and looking at him in a very friendly way.

"Good morning, little friend!" Sebastian's white teeth flashed and his dark eyes danced with laughter. "I am glad you came out from behind the flower to visit me."

He stroked the tiny creature gently with one finger. It felt like warm silk. It was so small and so perfect! Sebastian thanked God often for all the beautiful things He had put into the world.

All the animals loved Sebastian and he loved them. He loved all of the things God made because he loved God.

"Some day," Sebastian thought, "perhaps I can tell other people about how good God is. Right now, though, I must try to earn some money to help my father and mother."

Sebastian had several brothers and sisters, and his parents, Mr. and Mrs. Aparicio, were very poor. In Spain, when Sebastian was a boy, it was very hard for people to earn a living.

"Perhaps if I could go into the city I could earn money there," Sebastian thought. "I have seen people from the

city riding by. They have silver and fine leather on the horses and their clothing is made of satin and lace. They must have much money to buy such things and they might be glad to hire a strong boy like me. But I suppose I must wait until I am a little older."

So he worked hard and prayed hard for a few more years and then, when he was about sixteen, he went to the city. There was so much noise! There were so many people! He thought of how quiet it was at his home, of the fields where he tended sheep, of the friendly animals in the forests. He felt homesick for his parents and his brothers and sisters and he wondered how he could ever say his prayers in this noise and hurry.

But when he thought of his family he remembered that he had come to the city to earn money for them. Then they could have strong shoes and clothing without holes.

And sometimes, perhaps, his mother could buy meat for dinner. When he thought of all these good things he could do for them, he forgot how homesick he was.

Sebastian was a handsome boy and very strong and willing to work. He found work very soon.

"I will get him some good clothes," a rich man said to himself, "and he can attend me when I go out. Such a fine-looking servant will attract a good deal of attention."

Sebastian did not like life in the city. He did not like the way that people talked and acted. Most of all, he did not like the things that the women said about how handsome he was. They were always begging him to go to their parties and dances. When he would not, they made fun of him and asked him if he thought he was a saint.

But he kept on working and sending money to his family while the younger children grew up. Finally, his brothers were able to help their parents, and one of his sisters was old enough to leave home and get married.

Then at last, Sebastian decided to go back to the coun-

try and work in the fields, where he would have more time to say his prayers and to think about God.

The little wild animals all welcomed him, the birds sang special songs for him. Even the great gray wolf that frightened most people came quietly out of the woods and rubbed its head against Sebastian's knee. The lambs and the sheep would usually have run wildly away from the shaggy wolf, but this day they seemed to know he would not harm them. He was a friend of Sebastian, they could see, and Sebastian was their friend, too.

In the year 1518 everybody in Spain was excited. One of their brave sailors had discovered a new land, Mexico. The people in Spain liked to hear about Mexico: to hear of the beautiful buildings there, of the strange and wonderful things the people made from gold and silver and jewels.

Every year after that, more and more people went from Spain to see the new land, and when they came back they had exciting stories to tell. But it made Sebastian sad to think about the people in Mexico. They knew how to build beautiful temples, to paint pictures, and to carve stone in strange and wonderful shapes. But they did not know about God.

At last, when he was about thirty years old, Sebastian decided that he would go to Mexico, too. It would be hard to travel so far from his home, but he had the feeling that it was what God wanted him to do.

The ocean looked very big, and when he went aboard the ship seemed very small. And after they got away from the shore, it seemed as though the wind wanted to tear the sails to pieces. Dark waves pounded the sides of the little vessel and tossed it about so that Sebastian thought it would turn over and drown them all.

But at last, after many weary weeks, they reached

Mexico. Sebastian was sure it must be the most beautiful place on earth. There were high mountains and lakes, there were rivers and green valleys. Pine trees and oak trees grew in Mexico just as they did in Spain; but there were also mahogany and ebony trees and others that grow only in very hot climates.

And the birds! Usually in jungles the birds have bright feathers and are beautiful, but they do not sing. Here, in Mexico, there were more than twenty kinds of birds that were beautiful and sang, too.

Sebastian was happy to learn that in Mexico there were not only sheep and wolves such as he had known

in Spain, but many new kinds of animal friends as well.
There were beavers busily making their dams, and coyotes
building their strange little homes in the ground. From
treetops in the jungles, small, sad-faced monkeys looked
down and chattered to him as he passed. And one little
mother proudly held out her baby monkey for him to
admire.

The more Sebastian traveled around in Mexico, the better
he liked it. And the better he came to know the people, the

more he loved them. They were good and kind, and very, very hard-working. Sebastian was eager to tell them about God and His Mother. He wanted, too, to make their lives a little easier.

He settled down in the village called Puebla de los Angeles. Here most of the people supported themselves by raising fruits and vegetables. They sold these things in Mexico City, which was quite a distance away. The trip into the city was a hard one because the only path wound through forests and rough places and up and down hills. The people carried their loads in bundles on their backs, and by the time the poor, tired

travelers reached the market the fruits were often bruised
and the vegetables not very fresh.

"We should have a road going from here to the city,"
Sebastian said. "Then you could travel much more quickly
and easily. And if you didn't have to climb over rocks,
there wouldn't be so much danger of stepping on a rattle-
snake."

The people were surprised at such a plan. They knew that in some parts of Mexico there were roads. But the village of Puebla had never seen one.

"A road from our homes to the city?"

"Yes. Why not? I will show you how to build it and we can all work together on it. We will have it finished in no time."

Sebastian did not know much about how a road should be built, but he did know what it should look like. So he set to work and all the people helped him.

He cut down bushes and great trees that were in the way. The men helped him to roll big rocks off to one side. When they came to a place where the ground was always wet and muddy, he showed the people how to fill it up with rocks and stones. Then

he shoveled earth on top and all the men and women and children tramped on it until the dirt was packed down very smooth and hard.

At last the road was finished. Everyone was delighted.

"Now we can get to the city quickly," they said. "The fruit will still be juicy and the vegetables will be fresh when we try to sell them."

So the men and the women and the children tied up the

things they had to sell in long pieces of cloth. They hung these bundles on their backs like hammocks and hurried to town on the fine new road.

This road helped so many people that Sebastian decided there should be another one from the mines in the mountains down to the shore. And when that was done, he built another, and another, and another. He never took any pay for the work. He loved the Mexican people, and was happy to be able to help them in this way.

They were growing to love him, too. They loved him because he made their work easier; but they loved him even more because he was always ready to tell them about

Jesus and His Mother. They often asked to hear about the Baby born in a stable, the Baby Who was God. They listened carefully when Sebastian told them about good Saint Joseph, the carpenter, who worked hard to make a nice home for Mary and her Son. When they grew tired at their work they did not mind so much because they knew that Saint Joseph must have been very tired, too.

Sebastian sometimes thought, when he saw his Mexicans scratching up the earth for planting, that their ways of farming had not changed much since Saint Joseph's time.

"I will build a plow," he thought. "I can use it on my little farm, of course. But I can plow the other farms, too."

Men and women, boys and girls, all crowded around

when the plow was finished. It seemed very strange to
them to see this thing that cut through the earth the way
a ship cuts through water. And it was so easy! The man
had only to hold the plow's handles and push – and the
earth was all ready for planting.

But when Sebastian let one of the big boys try to plow,
he found it was not so easy. The plow did not want to keep
its nose in the ground. It did not want to go in a straight
line.

"It is something you must learn," Sebastian told them. "There are rules for plowing a field and rules for getting to Heaven. You must learn them both, and obey them."

The plow made a great difference in the crops. Now the people were able to grow more things. They staggered under the heavy loads of food they carried into the city. So Sebastian began to talk about making wagons for them.

They were puzzled when Sebastian told them about the sort of wagon people used in Spain.

"It rolls like a round stone down the mountain?" they asked. "But how do you throw it back up again?"

"Your donkey pulls it," Sebastian told them.

"But how can a little donkey pull it? He has no hands!"

Sebastian laughed.

"You harness the donkey to the wagon."

"What is a harness?" they asked.

"I will show you all about it," Sebastian promised.

The next day he took a group of men from the village out to the forest to chop trees. They cut them into logs, and split the logs into planks to build the body of the wagon.

"But this is not round!" The men were disappointed. "It will not roll down the hill."

Then Sebastian taught them how to build wheels, and axles for the wheels to turn on. They fastened the axles to the body of the wagon.

The men were delighted and called their families to come and see. Mothers and fathers, sons and daughters, all took turns sitting in the wagon while the others pulled them across the field.

"Now the harness will have to be made," said Sebastian. "I have some fine, strong cowhide we can use."

The men watched with interest as he cut and shaped the pieces, sewing them over and over so they would be firm and strong. When it was done he took two of his donkeys to harness them.

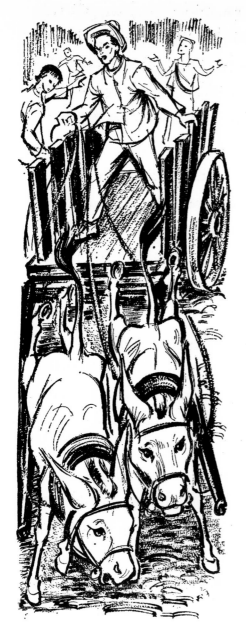

The little animals stood still while Sebastian harnessed them. They were used to carrying heavy loads on their backs. But when he hitched them to the wagon, they didn't know just what was going on. And when he started to lead them, they didn't like at all to have the wagon pulling them back and coming along right behind them.

"Hee-haw! Hee-haw!" they brayed. And they kicked up their heels to try to stop the wagon from following them.

Sebastian spoke to them softly.

"Don't be afraid, little donkeys," he said. "The wagon will not hurt you. This is your work now, and you must get used to it."

The donkeys looked at Sebastian with their big, soft eyes and turned their long ears to catch his words. They seemed to understand what he was saying, and they were anxious to please him. So when he started walking again they allowed themselves to be led along with the wagon rolling behind them.

The people now had roads and a wagon. Soon there were many little wagons going up and down the hills, to and from the city. Sebastian built another wagon for himself and used it to carry things for people. If the people were rich, he would ask them to pay him. But if they were poor, he was always glad to do it for nothing.

One day Sebastian was working in the fields when a neighbor passed, driving his wagon to market.

"Good morning, Sebastian," he called.

"Good morning, Juan. You are getting your corn into market early."

"This is only part of the crop," said Juan. "Since you plowed my fields for me and showed me how to tend them, I get a great deal more corn than I used to."

"I am glad of that," said Sebastian. "What are you going to do with the rest of the corn?"

"When I have unloaded this in the market, I will come back for the rest. My little donkey will have to make two trips today."

Sebastian looked at the little beast. It was very old, he knew, and not as strong as it used to be. The trip to the city and back was a long, hard one. To make it twice in one day was a big task for even a strong young animal.

"If you had a bigger wagon you could take all the corn in one trip," said Sebastian.

"But the old one could not pull more than he has here," Juan said.

"I know! I know!" said Sebastian. "I was not thinking of piling more of a load on this good old worker."

He did not speak for a while.

"If we were to make quite a large wagon we could have oxen —"

Juan did not let him finish what he was saying.

"Oxen, Sebastian? You might as well think of using eagles from the air! They are all wild creatures and work is not for them."

"Perhaps," said Sebastian, "but I do not think so."

Juan drove off to the city shaking his head. Sebastian was good and kind and generous. He knew about the Holy Family and the Way to Heaven and would tell about them whenever he was asked. But, Juan thought sadly, Sebastian was going crazy. For it surely was crazy to think of taking those fierce, heavy wild oxen and using them as if they were little gray donkeys!

But Sebastian set to work building the wagon. It was more than twice the size of those pulled by the donkeys. Instead of shafts like the ones on the small wagon, this had a long pole sticking out in front. And the harness Sebastian made was different, too. There was a wooden thing he called a yoke that was to go across the necks of the oxen. It would keep one from walking faster than the other and doing all the work.

When the village people learned what Sebastian was planning to do, they grew very frightened. Oxen were big, powerful animals whom very few people dared to go near. They were raised mostly for their meat and their hides, and when it was time to get them in from the fields only the bravest men were sent to rope them.

"I will pray to Our Lady Mary that nothing happens to Sebastian," said one of the women. Sebastian had taught her her religion.

"I will pray to Saint Joseph," said the woman's husband, who was a carpenter.

Their little boy spoke up.

"I will pray to the Baby Jesus," he said. "He will not let anything happen to Sebastian. I love Sebastian."

When everything was ready, Sebastian went out to the fields where the oxen were grazing. They saw a man coming toward them, and could hardly believe it. They pawed the ground angrily and snorted so hard they blew up great

clouds of dust. Their little eyes got red and they shook their heads to show off their cruel horns.

But this man did not grow frightened and run, as men always had before. He came steadily onward, talking quietly to them all the while.

"Don't get so excited, my friends," he said. "You are big strong creatures, I know. And I think it is about time you used your strength to help people."

The oxen put down their heads so that their sharp horns pointed straight at Sebastian. Those horns could go right through a man. But Sebastian just kept on walking toward them. The oxen did not move. When he reached the place where they were standing, he took hold of the horns of two of them.

"Come with me," he said. "I will teach you your new duties."

The oxen did not want to be harnessed nor to have the heavy yoke across their shoulders. But though they pulled and fussed, they never tried to hurt Sebastian. And at last they agreed to pull the big wagon, and were put to work.

At night, when the day's tasks were done, Sebastian let them go back to the fields. Then they seemed just as wild and just as fierce as they used to be. But when Sebastian went for them in the morning, they came with him quietly and resumed their work.

Sebastian built more wag-
ons and trained more oxen.
Some were for other people,
but several Sebastian kept for
himself. More and more rich
people were settling in Mexico
now, and they were glad to
pay Sebastian to carry their
goods and to plow their fields.
So, although he gave away
great quantities of money, he
himself grew rich.

When a young couple
wanted to get married, Sebastian would give them money
enough to start a new home.
Sometimes a poor man would
be put in jail for a reason that
seemed unfair to Sebastian.
Then Sebastian would pay his
fine so that he could go back
to his family.

But one thing worried this good man. He could teach
the children who lived near him — but who would teach
Catechism to the many children in Mexico City? And who
was there who could take care of the old and the sick?
He was very unhappy about this until at last he had a
chance to bring a convent of Poor Clare nuns over from
Europe, to teach and to nurse. He began building their new
home with his own hands.

The years went by. The little boys and girls who had
first learned about God from Sebastian were men and

women now, with children of their own. These children could hardly believe that there had been no wagons at Puebla de los Angeles before Sebastian came. Almost everyone had a wagon now. And they laughed when their fathers told them about scratching up the fields for planting. Imagine using a stick instead of a plow! But every morning and every night they prayed for Sebastian because he was the one who had taught their parents about God and how to pray to Him.

When Sebastian was seven-
ty-eight years old, he made
another plan. This time it
was not for a road to town,
but a plan to help him on the
road to Heaven. He gave away
his farms to families who
were too poor to have farms
of their own. He gave away

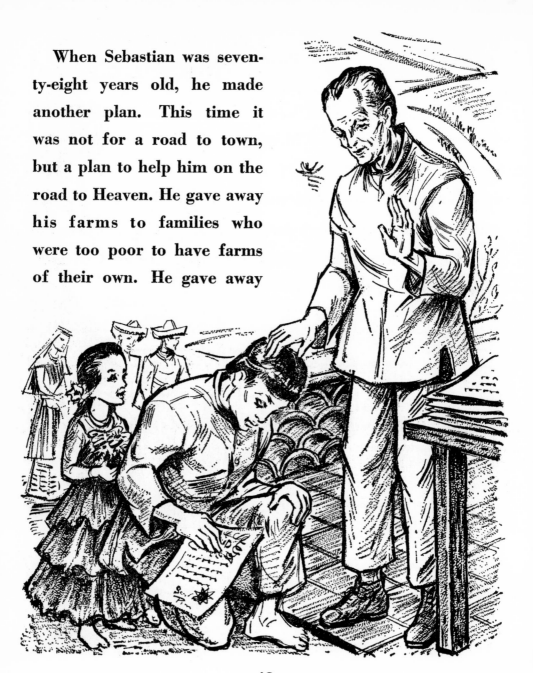

all his money to the Poor Clares so they could help even more people. Then he went to live at a Franciscan Monastery.

"I know I am much too old to study for the priesthood," he told the priest at the head of the monastery. "And anyway I am not nearly good enough. But there must be some work I could do here."

The priest was very glad to have him to help them, and he invited Sebastian to become a Franciscan Brother.

One of his duties was to go around begging food for the Franciscans. He had to travel many miles, often on foot. His days were long and hard, but

he was happier than he had ever been before. He ate very little food and at night he slept on the floor with a stone for his pillow. Often at night he did not sleep at all, but would go quietly down to the chapel to visit with Christ, Who waited so patiently there in the Tabernacle.

Even when he was more than ninety years old, he went out every day on his business of getting food. Most of the time he walked beside his oxen. Sometimes when he was very tired he would stumble on his torn sandals and fall against the huge animals. They would stop at once for fear they might step on this gentle man whom they loved

and served. No matter how badly they might act with any-
one else, when Sebastian drove them they were always quiet
and obedient.

At last, when he was nearly a hundred years old, Sebastian could not go out any more. He was in great pain and
he knew that his illness had no cure. He could not even go
as far as the garden to say his prayers, and the little birds
which used to perch on his shoulder there seemed to miss
him.

Then, one day, God took his soul to Heaven.

When the Mexican people heard that Sebastian was dead, they were very sad. Men and women, boys and girls, traveled many, many miles to say good-by to the man who had loved them and whom they loved. Some of the people walked, others came on donkey-back. But most of them came in the wagons Sebastian had taught them to build.

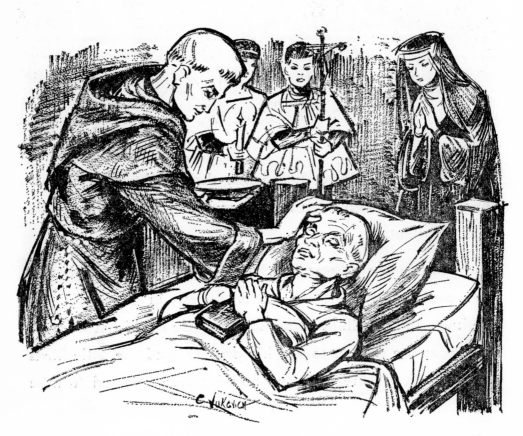

All through Mexico there were good things to remember Sebastian by. The people drove their oxen, and they knew they would never have dared to do that if Sebastian had not done it first. Many of them knew about God because Sebastian had taught them or taught their parents.

The poor and the sick began to pray to Sebastian, asking him to speak to God for them. Then, as time went on, many people told their priests and bishops about the help that came when they asked for it from their good friend in Heaven. All the letters and accounts of these wonderful things were sent to Rome to be carefully read and thought over. Finally the Pope said that all this proved that Sebastian was truly a holy friend of God; he would be called Blessed Sebastian and his feast day would be celebrated on February twenty-fifth.

Some people speak of Blessed Sebastian as "The Road Builder" because he made so many fine roads for the Mexican people. But usually we think of Blessed Sebastian with the oxen, the big animals he trained to help him work for men and God.

EVA K. BETZ'S Easy Reading Books of

SAINTS AND FRIENDLY BEASTS

SAINT GERMAINE AND THE SHEEP

Germaine was not a pretty child but she was a happy one. Her family was not kind to her but God showed His love for her in many ways. And when she wanted to call on Him in church, the sheep helped her to do so.

SAINT COLUM AND THE CRANE

Young Colum was the son of a king. He could have been the leader of an army but he decided instead to become a warrior for God. As a young boy, as a student for the priesthood, and as a wise teacher, he had a friend — a great crane — that stayed always near him.

BLESSED SEBASTIAN AND THE OXEN

Blessed Sebastian wanted to help the poor people of Mexico. He taught them to make plows and wagons and dared to get the great wild oxen in from the fields to pull the things he built. The animals knew that Sebastian was good and kind so they helped him gladly.

All profusely illustrated by Charles B. Vukovich